GARFIELD
ANNUAL

Created by
JIM DAVIS
Written by
Gordon Volke
RAVETTE
BOOKS

CONTENTS

Published by Ravette Books Limited 1991

Printed and bound for Ravette Books Limited,
3 Glenside Estate, Star Road, Partridge Green,
Horsham, West Sussex RH13 8RA.
An Egmont Company
by
Proost International Bookproduction.

ISBN: 1 85304 343 5

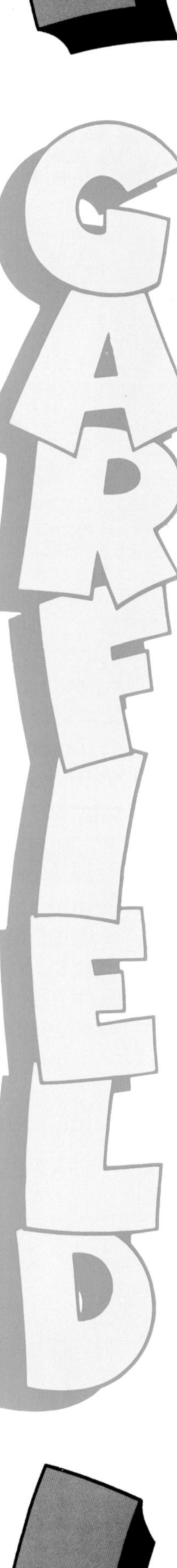
GARFIELD

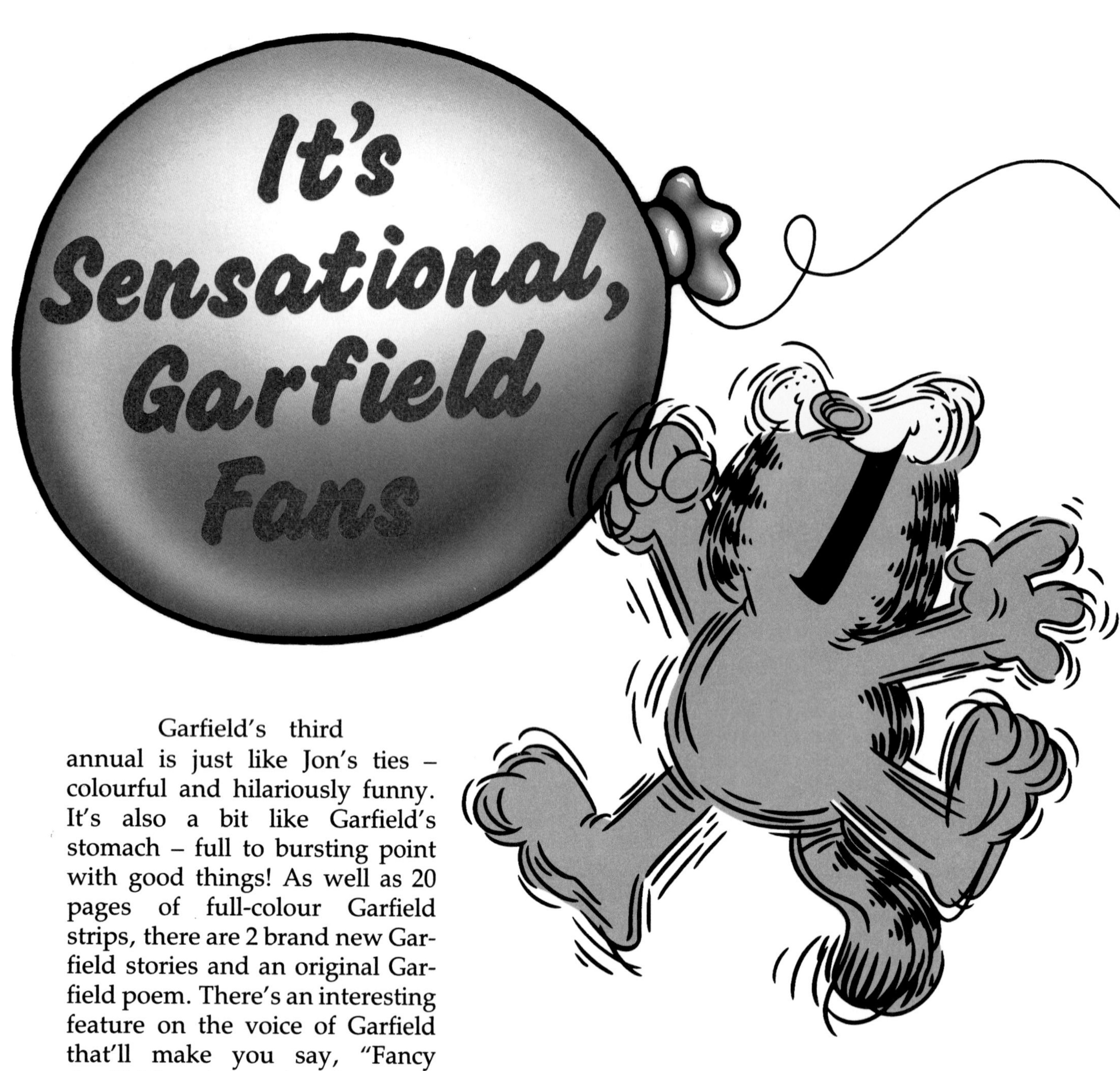

Garfield's third annual is just like Jon's ties – colourful and hilariously funny. It's also a bit like Garfield's stomach – full to bursting point with good things! As well as 20 pages of full-colour Garfield strips, there are 2 brand new Garfield stories and an original Garfield poem. There's an interesting feature on the voice of Garfield that'll make you say, "Fancy that!" There's another fascinating feature on exotic spiders that'll also make you say, "Fancy that!" Alternatively, it might make you say, "ARRRGH!"

In addition to all this, there are 3 superb bound-in posters, a wide variety of activity pages including a fun quiz and lots of puzzles, plus a special Garfield glossary – a useful guide to American expressions which should fascinate all you Garfield buffs.

All in all, the GARFIELD ANNUAL is a real feast of entertainment.

DROP IN ON THE FUN!

A FRIDGE TOO FAR

"Where are you going, Garfield?" asked Jon.

"Up the Amazon," replied Garfield. "Then I thought I'd pop over to India in my private jet and do the Taj Mahal."

"You're going into the kitchen, aren't you, Garfield?" said Jon.

"Your powers of observation astound me, Holmes!" murmured Garfield.

"Why are you going into the kitchen, Garfield?" asked Jon.

"I'm going to give a pop concert to an audience of 100,000," said Garfield.

"You're after more food, aren't you, Garfield?" exclaimed Jon.

"Got it in one, buddy boy!" cried Garfield.

Jon planted himself in front of the fridge and folded his arms. "No, Garfield," he said.

"Nice one, Jon," laughed Garfield, trying to push his master out of the way. "Now let the dog see the rabbit, if you'll pardon the expression."

"I'm serious, Garfield," insisted Jon. "You've already had 12 hamburgers, 27 rounds of buttered toast, 6 king-sized pizzas and a 3 litre tub of ice-cream – and it isn't even lunchtime yet. You're getting nothing else today except black coffee!"

"With sugar?" asked Garfield.

"Without sugar!" said Jon.

Garfield stomped back into the sitting-room and flopped down in front of the TV. Idly, his eyes flicked up at the screen. A fox was crawling stealthily through some long grass. "It's one of those Nature programmes," yawned Garfield. "The fox," said the voice of the TV commentator, "gets all its food by raiding. It is a very cunning animal," Garfield sat up with interest. "You ain't seen nothin' yet!" he grinned.

Garfield dived into his box and pulled the covers over his head. He waited until he heard Jon coming into the room. Jon was carrying a delicious-looking pie and walking like a sneak-thief. "Don't want Garfield to see me eating this!" he murmured.

Garfield struck like lightning! Shooting out of his box like a rocket, he crossed the room in a series of bounds and snatched the pie out of Jon's hand. Garfield devoured it in a split second. "Not bad," he commented. "But I prefer short-crust to puff pastry!"

After his successful raid, Garfield beat a hasty retreat. Having laid low for half an hour, however, he began to feel hungry again. "Have to go on another excursion," he muttered. So Garfield crawled across the floor, belly-down style, and hid behind the sofa.

"Doing an impression of a beached whale, Garfield?" asked Jon. "Don't ruin my act!" snapped Garfield.

"You won't be able to steal any more food," added Jon. "I've hidden it!"

Garfield came out of hiding. He spotted a sausage that Jon had dropped on the floor. He was about to devour it when he stopped. "'Box clever', the man said," he chuckled. Garfield went to find Odie who was chasing his tail in the garden. "Here, slobberchops!" he called.

Garfield gave Odie the sausage to sniff. "Now go find the others!" he ordered. Barking excitedly, Odie rushed off – straight into the wall of the house. "Use the door, bone-breath!" yelled Garfield.

Odie led Garfield to the cupboard under the stairs. "Thanks, pal," cried Garfield. "Here's your reward." Odie expected to be given the sausage, but Garfield just patted his friend on the head and ate the sausage himself. Then he set about the food hidden in the cupboard. He ate it all in seconds. "Not bad," he burped, "but the cookies had raisins in them. Suppose I must get used to living off the land."

Garfield continued his raids all day. By late afternoon, there was nothing left in the house. Garfield was beginning to worry about evening starvation when a delivery van pulled up at the gate. "Thanks for coming, boys!" called Jon, as two burly delivery men struggled in with a huge fridge. Garfield noticed that the fridge door was fitted with a combination lock. "How low can you get!" he muttered.

Garfield waited until it was dark and then took up position on the garden fence. "Let's hear it for New Kits On The Block!" he called, starting to wail the latest pop song.

Ignoring the volley of shoes from the neighbours, Garfield continued making a noise like a tribe of banshees on a train with rusty brakes.

"Stoppit!" yelled Jon at last.

"Only if you give me the combination of that fridge," snapped Garfield.

"It's a deal!" cried Jon. "19-6-78!"

"My birthday," grinned Garfield. "How very appropriate!"

Garfield twiddled the lock of the fridge and the big, heavy door swung open. He looked at the array of food Jon had put inside. "Time for some speed-eating," he chuckled.

Garfield powered his way through the fridge, taking each shelf in turn. Once or twice, he thought some items tasted a little strange, but he paid no attention.

"I'm into quantity, not quality," he mumbled.

By the time he had finished, Garfield's stomach was nearly as big as the fridge. "No more Binky the Clown for me," he sighed, contentedly. "I'm watching Nature shows from now on!"

Shortly afterwards, Garfield's stomach started to gurgle. It sounded like the water running out of a million bathtubs.

"Help, help!" yelled Garfield. "Mike Tyson's going 15 rounds inside my small intestine!"

Jon sauntered in looking far from worried.

"Tummy ache, Garfield?" he inquired.

"No, groaned Garfield. "I'm a Sixties freak doing the Twist!"

"I win, Garfield," laughed Jon, bending down and looking his pet in the eye. "I knew you'd find a way to get into that fridge, so I filled it with **fake** food. I got it from the theatrical shop in town."

"You mean . . . ?" spluttered Garfield.

"It was all made of WAX!" chortled Jon.

"At least my insides will be clean and shiny," muttered Garfield.

Jon left Garfield in the kitchen and went upstairs to bed. "That cat doesn't know the meaning of 'cunning'," he chuckled. Jon had just settled down with his book, 'The Advanced Guide to Bad Taste', when he heard noises coming from below. "I'd better go down and see if Garfield's all right," thought Jon. "I'd hate anything to happen to him!"

Jon opened the kitchen door and peeped inside. Garfield was tucking into a cheese and tomato pizza he had stolen from the larder.

"But I thought . . ." began Jon.

"We speed-eaters have amazing powers of recovery," said Garfield. Jon watched incredulously as Garfield swallowed the last of the pizza. "All I can say," commented Jon, "is that you'd better not watch any more programmes about foxes."

"Wouldn't dream of it," replied Garfield. "There's one on tomorrow about sharks!"

© 1987 United Feature Syndicate, Inc.

AMUSED, GARFIELD?
THAT'S "MR. FIG FACE" TO YOU
JIM DAVIS 1-26

♪

JIM DAVIS 1-27

♫

HERE I AM FALLING ASLEEP FACE DOWN IN A BOWL OF FOOD

THIS IS IT. I'VE REACHED THE PINNACLE OF LAZINESS AND GLUTTONY... HOW DEPRESSING

THERE'S NO PLACE TO GO AFTER YOU'VE REACHED THE TOP
JIM DAVIS 1-28

I EAT TOO MUCH BECAUSE I'M DEPRESSED, AND I'M DEPRESSED BECAUSE I EAT TOO MUCH
GARFIELD

IT'S A VICIOUS CIRCLE...
GARFIELD

THAT TOOK YEARS TO PERFECT!
JIM DAVIS 1-29

Another day, another swaller!

LOOK, ODIE! A HIDEOUS HAIRY MONSTER IS NESTING UNDER JON'S NOSE!
JIM DAVIS 1-21

MAYBE IT'LL SPREAD AND COVER THE REST OF HIS FACE

ARE YOU MAKING FUN OF ME?
IT MOVED!

MUSTACHES DO STRANGE THINGS TO PEOPLE
1-22 JIM DAVIS

THEY MAKE SOME GUYS THINK THEY'RE SOMEONE THEY'RE NOT

FRANKLY, MY DEAR, I DON'T GIVE A DARN
I DON'T FEEL SAFE HERE ANYMORE

ARRRGH!
JIM DAVIS 1-23

JON! WHAT HAPPENED?
I'M FINE! GO AWAY!

ARE YOU OKAY? TELL ME!
THE SHAVER SNAGGED MY MUSTACHE, OKAY?

I SHAVED MY MUSTACHE OFF, GARFIELD
DO TELL
JIM DAVIS 1-24

I DECIDED IT MADE ME LOOK LIKE A WALRUS
I'M PROUD OF YOU, JON

IT TAKES A BIG WALRUS TO ADMIT HIS MISTAKES

AH, MY DEAR, YOU'RE AS LOVELY AS EVER. BUT, YOU LOOK SO STIFF AND FORMAL IN THAT OUTFIT

WHY DON'T YOU SLIP INTO SOMETHING MORE COMFORTABLE?

LIKE ME!
JIM DAVIS 1-14

JIM DAVIS 1-15

CHOMP!

SPRONG!

JUST WHAT IS AN HEIRLOOM?

AN HEIRLOOM IS SOMETHING THAT'S BEEN IN YOUR FAMILY FOR GENERATIONS...

THAT NO ONE'S HAD THE GUTS TO PITCH OUT

JUST AS I SUSPECTED

Flower Power!

Garfield has come up with 20 words beginning with the letters CAT. Using the clues to help you, can you complete the words?
Answers on page 56.

1. CAT _ _ _ _ _ _ _ _
Turns into butterfly or moth

2. CAT _ _ _ _ _ _ _ _
A terrible disaster

3. CAT _ _ _
Collection of cows or oxon

4. CAT _ _ _ _ _ _
List of information or things to buy

5. CAT'_ _ _ _ _ _ _
Children's game played with string (2 words)

6. CAT _ _ _ _ _ _ _ _
A well-known saying

7. CAT _ _ _ _ _ _
A large church

8. CAT _ _ _ _ _
Made from strong twig and elastic

9. CAT _ _ _ _ _ _
Type of boat, usually with two hulls

10. CAT _ _ _
Flower of willow or hazel tree

11. CAT _ _ _ _ _
Underground burial chamber

12. CAT _ _ _ _ _ _ _ _ _ _ _
A spinning firework (2 words)

13. CAT _ _ _ _ _
Food and drink for a party

14. CAT _ _ _ _
Shout or whistle of disapproval

15. CAT _ _ _ _
A runny nose!

16. CAT _ _ _ _ _
A group or classification

17. CAT _ _
You do this with a ball

18. CAT –' _ _ _ _
Little reflectors in middle of the road

19. CAT _ _ _ _ _
A big waterfall or a problem with the eye

20. CAT _ _ _ _ _ _
To scream or make a horrible noise

The VOICE of Garfield

Actor, writer, producer and all-round funny man, LORENZO MUSIC is the voice of Garfield.

One day during the late 1970s, Jim Davis was at home working on his new comic strip, Garfield. The cartoonist liked to have the television on while he worked and one of the shows that appeared was a sit-com called 'Rhoda'. Rhoda, a girl from Minneapolis now living in New York, had a doorman named Carlton. You never saw Carlton, you only ever heard his voice saying:

"Hello, this is Carlton your doorman."

As soon as Jim Davis heard Carlton's voice, he knew it was exactly right for Garfield. The part of Carlton was played by Lorenzo Music.

When Jim Davis came to produce his first Garfield TV special, 'Here Comes Garfield', he invited Lorenzo Music to audition for the part of the fat cat. The job has been his ever since. Anyone who has watched the series of award-winning TV specials that followed, or the popular TV series 'Garfield and Friends', will have heard "the sound of Music!"

This instant success was no flash-in-the-pan. Behind it lies a long and distinguished career in American show business. Lorenzo Music was born in New York and brought up in Minnesota. At Minnesota University, he met his wife and they formed a comedy duo, performing at clubs and colleges during the 'folk boom' of the early 1960s. The arrival of the first of their 4 children put an end of 'Jerry and Myrna Music', as their act was called, and Lorenzo Music turned his attention to writing.

It was a natural progression for the humorous and talented young man. In 1968, after only one year on the writing staff of the TV show, 'The Smothers Brothers Comedy Hour', Lorenzo Music won an Emmy (the television equivalent of an Oscar) for 'outstanding achievement in comedy writing'. During the 1970s he went on to write, edit, and produce a long series of classic TV comedy shows, many of which have been shown in this country. The list includes 'The Mary Tyler Moore Show', 'The Bob Newhart Show' and the aforementioned 'Rhoda'.

Then came Garfield, and the rest as they say, is history.

Nowadays, Lorenzo Music lives in Los Angeles where he continues to work in the field of comedy. It is his distinctive voice, however, that is most in demand. As well as Garfield, he is the voice of Tummy Gummi in 'The Gummi Bears' and Peter Venkman in 'The Real Ghostbusters'. In addition to all this cartoon work, he has recorded countless radio and TV commercials, making him one of the best-known voices in the field of American advertising.

No doubt by now you are wondering what this multi-talented showbiz personality looks like. Until recently you would have remained in the dark because Lorenzo Music was always reluctant to show his face in public. Why? Because he felt that to let people see what he looked like would destroy the illusion created by his voice. He once explained:

"If people saw a picture of me, they would say, "He looks like *that* instead of Garfield!" If you have a visual image, it takes away from what you hear."

However, we are very pleased to say that Mr Music has set aside these reservations and provided the Garfield Annual with a splendid picture of himself. So, for the very first time, we present the Voice of Garfield and the Face of Garfield!

FAST FOOD QUIZ

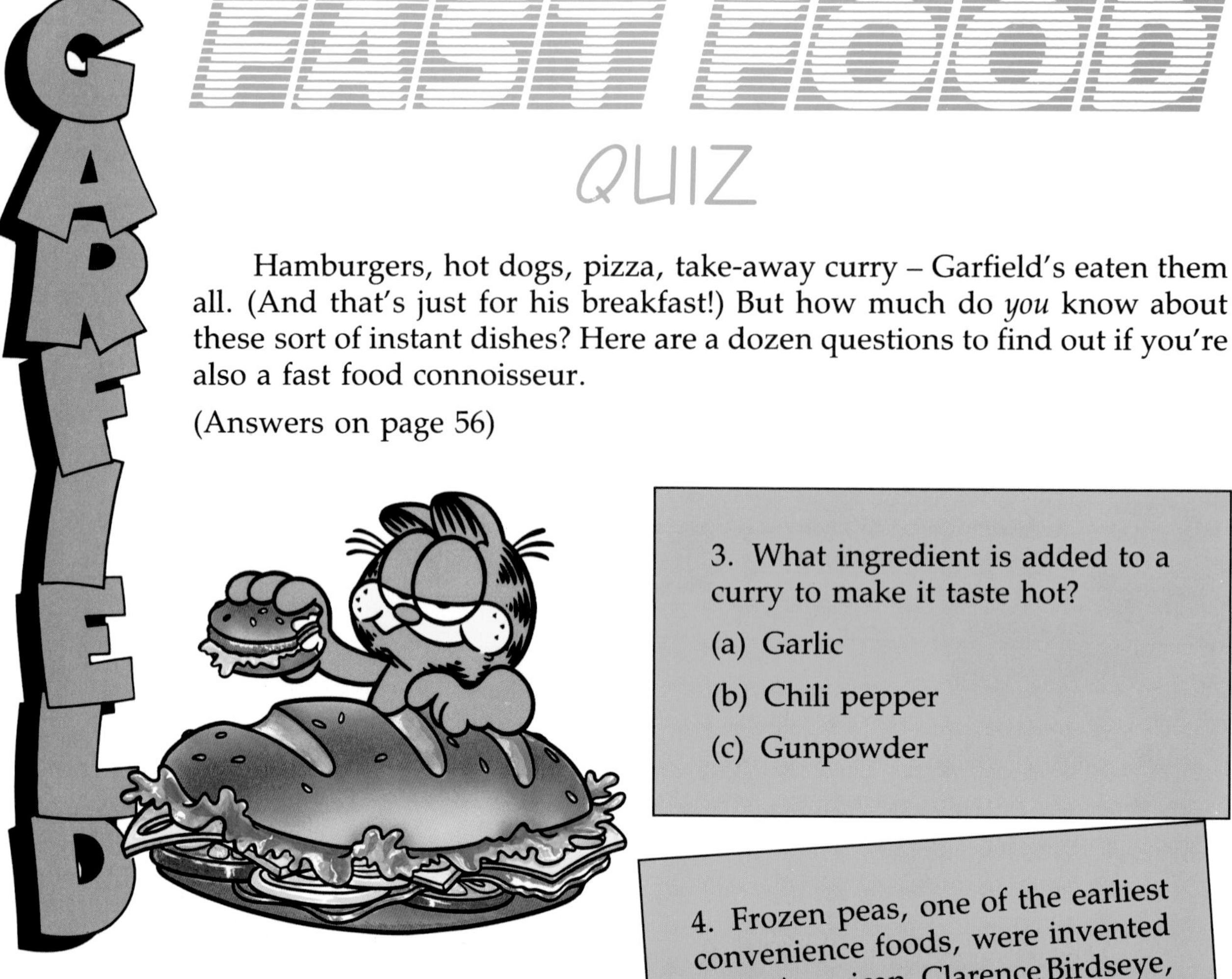

Hamburgers, hot dogs, pizza, take-away curry – Garfield's eaten them all. (And that's just for his breakfast!) But how much do *you* know about these sort of instant dishes? Here are a dozen questions to find out if you're also a fast food connoisseur.

(Answers on page 56)

1. In which country was the pizza invented?

(a) France

(b) Italy

(c) Spain

(d) Iceland

2. If you ordered a vindaloo curry from an Indian take-away, would it be:

(a) Mild?

(b) Medium?

(c) Hot?

(d) So hot it makes your eyes stand out on stalks?

3. What ingredient is added to a curry to make it taste hot?

(a) Garlic

(b) Chili pepper

(c) Gunpowder

4. Frozen peas, one of the earliest convenience foods, were invented by an American, Clarence Birdseye, in 1930.

(a) True?

(b) False?

5. What is the main ingredient of the Chinese dish, chop suey?

(a) Beansprouts

(b) Noodles

(c) Chop sticks

6. What sort of sausage is used in a hot dog?

(a) Frankfurter

(b) Chipolata

(c) Garlic sausage

(d) Dachshund

7. Which character in Popeye cartoons is always eating hamburgers?

(a) Bluto

(b) Olive Oyl

(c) Wimpy

8. One type of take-away food has been available in this country for many years and is traditionally British. What is it?

9. Can you complete this sentence? 'Pieces of meat and vegetable, mounted on a skewer and grilled, are known as a _ _ _ _ _.'

10. Sandwiches are named after the 4th Earl of Sandwich who, in 1762, spent a whole day and night playing cards and ate nothing but slices of meat pressed between pieces of bread.

(a) True?

(b) False?

11. Which best-selling soft drink was invented by an American doctor, John S. Pemberton, and originally sold as a tonic?

(a) Lemonade

(b) Coca-Cola

(c) Mineral water

(d) Tonic water

(e) Ginger beer

12. If Garfield was given a 'knickerbocker glory', would he be pleased? Can you say why?

YOU SAY LASAGNA AND WE SAY LASAGNE...

A Garfield Glossary

Have you ever read a Garfield strip and thought, "Hey! There's a spelling mistake in this!" Well, there isn't! The problem arises from the fact that Garfield originates in America and the words in the speech balloons contain American English. So, for future reference, here is a selection of American words and phrases that crop up most often in the strips and an explanation of their meaning in the UK.

The Great Lasagne Debate

In America, Garfield's favourite food is spelt with an 'a': LASAGNA.

In Britain, it is spelt with an 'e': LASAGNE.

Very often you will find BOTH spellings within the same publication. This is because the strips are always published with Jim Davis's original lettering in the speech balloons, whereas the other pages containing the editorial features are written on this side of the Atlantic.

So now you know!

Mall-function!

When Garfield buys something, he goes to the MALL. In this country we would call it the SHOPPING PRECINCT or possibly the HIGH STREET.

(The word 'mall' originated in England and used to mean the alley in which the game of 'pall-mall' was played. The word crossed the Atlantic and now means any long parade of shops. We still use the word here in the famous London street names of The Mall and Pall Mall.)

Hubert and Reba had gone to the THEATER/THEATRE. "I'm being a good NEIGHBOR/NEIGHBOUR," said Jon," and checking their house is all right." Garfield went next door with Jon.

"Isn't their lounge a lovely COLOR/COLOUR!" exclaimed Jon.

"Purple with pink stripes," muttered Garfield. "Exquisite!" Garfield wandered off and ate the fern in the CENTER/CENTRE of the table."I can't take you anywhere, Garfield!" yelled Jon. "That was their FAVORITE/FAVOURITE houseplant!"

Jon sent Garfield home in disgrace. 'That man has no sense of HUMOR/HUMOUR!" grumbled Garfield.

Transatlantic Translations

YARD	GARDEN
SIDEWALK	PAVEMENT
DIAPER	NAPPY
LEASH	LEAD
A TAD	A LITTLE BIT
SHEDDING	MOULTING
POTATO CHIPS	CRISPS
FALL	AUTUMN
FAUCET	TAP
CATSUP	KETCHUP or SAUCE
CLOSET	WARDROBE

The following words do NOT change . . .
Fat, greedy, lazy, lovable, funny, grumpy, sarcastic, appealing, self-centred, conceited and great.

Arlene's Beauty Wordsearch

Here are 20 items which Arlene uses to make herself look beautiful. 19 of them are printed in the grid. They read forwards, backwards, up, down and diagonally. They always go in a straight line and never skip any letters.

Can you find them?

When you have finished, can you say which is the missing item?

Solution on page 56

LIPSTICK	**BLUSHER**	**NECKLACE**	**SHAMPOO**
FACE CREAM	**EAR RING**	**BRACELET**	**CONDITIONER**
EYE SHADOW	**STUD**	**BANGLE**	**TALC**
			PERFUME
			BATH SALTS
			HANDBAG
			SHOES
			HAT
			SCARF
			GLOVES
			MASCARA

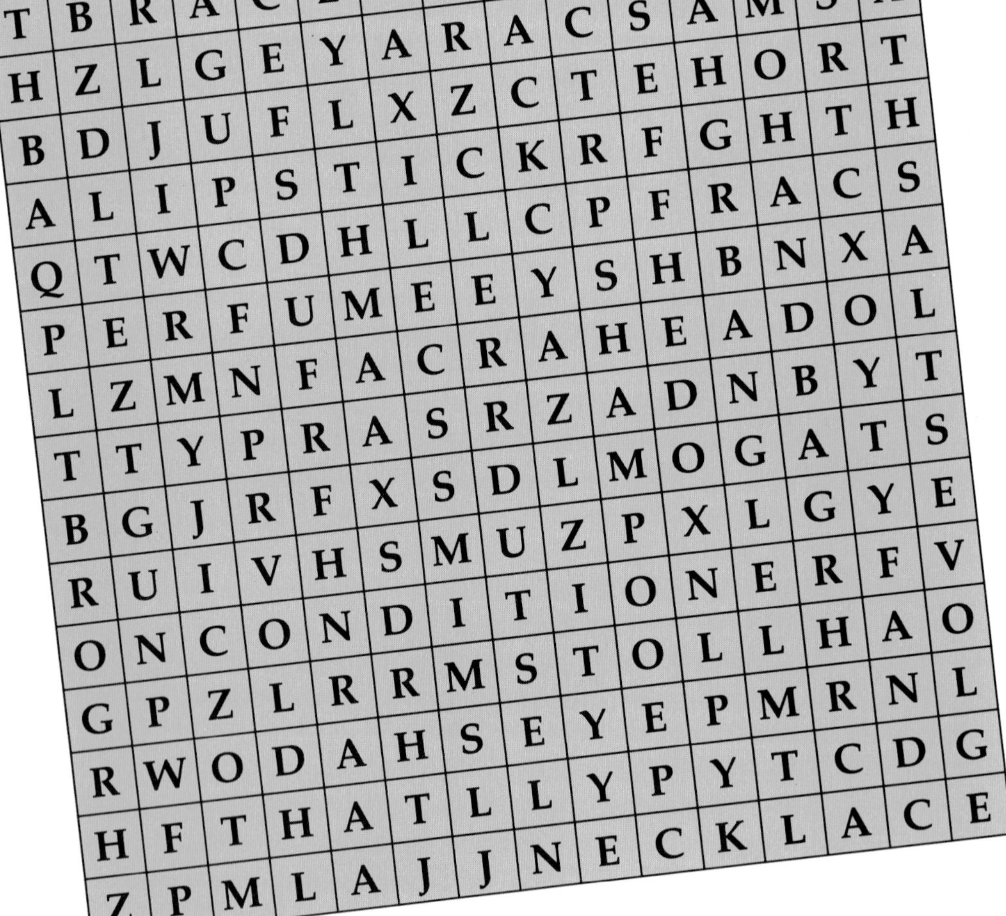

T	B	R	A	C	E	L	E	T	X	Y	O	M	P	B
H	Z	L	G	E	Y	A	R	A	C	S	A	M	S	A
B	D	J	U	F	L	X	Z	C	T	E	H	O	R	T
A	L	I	P	S	T	I	C	K	R	F	G	H	T	H
Q	T	W	C	D	H	L	L	C	P	F	R	A	C	S
P	E	R	F	U	M	E	E	Y	S	H	B	N	X	A
L	Z	M	N	F	A	C	R	A	H	E	A	D	O	L
T	T	Y	P	R	A	S	R	Z	A	D	N	B	Y	T
B	G	J	R	F	X	S	D	L	M	O	G	A	T	S
R	U	I	V	H	S	M	U	Z	P	X	L	G	Y	E
O	N	C	O	N	D	I	T	I	O	N	E	R	F	V
G	P	Z	L	R	R	M	S	T	O	L	L	H	A	O
R	W	O	D	A	H	S	E	Y	E	P	M	R	N	L
H	F	T	H	A	T	L	L	Y	P	Y	T	C	D	G
Z	P	M	L	A	J	J	N	E	C	K	L	A	C	E

GARFIELD
HA! HA! HA! HEE! HA!

NAH, NAH, NAH, NAH, NAH, NAAAAH

WE'RE GOING FOR A WALK, AND YOU HAVE TO WEAR A DOG COAT
© 1987 United Feature Syndicate, Inc.

WE'RE GONNA WALK BY SOME DOGS, AND THEY'RE GONNA CALL YOU A NERD

NAH. NAH, NAH, NAH, NAH, NAAAAH

COME ON, GARFIELD. LET'S GET READY FOR OUR WALK
JIM DAVIS 3-29

MAYBE LIGHTNING WILL STRIKE ME, AND SAVE ME THE HUMILIATION

JIM DAVIS 2-2

BONK!

GARFIELD! SPEAK TO ME!
AUNTY EM? IS THAT YOU?

GARFIELD! THAT WAS A NASTY FALL YOU TOOK. ARE YOU ALL RIGHT?
JIM DAVIS 2-3

GARFIELD? WHO'S GARFIELD?

OH, NO! HE'S LOST HIS MEMORY!
I DO SEEM TO REMEMBER BEING HUNGRY

HAVING AMNESIA ISN'T SO BAD. IT'LL BE KIND OF FUN FINDING OUT WHAT A GREAT GUY I AM
JIM DAVIS 2-4

ARRRGH!

OH, NO! I'M A CAT!

MAYBE SEEING ODIE WILL JOG YOUR MEMORY
WHAT A SWELL LOOKING DOG. PUT 'ER THERE

YIP! YIP! YIP!

I WONDER IF I'M GOING TO LIKE THIS GARFIELD?
JIM DAVIS 2-5

LOOK, GARFIELD. IT'S POOKY! YOUR FAVORITE POSSESSION AND CLOSEST FRIEND. DO YOU REMEMBER POOKY?
JIM DAVIS 2-6

DON'T BE SILLY. I'M A GROWN CAT. WHAT WOULD I NEED WITH A TEDDY BEAR?

AMNESIA HAS WIPED MY SLATE CLEAN. I START ESTABLISHING WHO I AM TODAY
JIM DAVIS 2-7

I AM (BURP) A GLUTTON

AMNESIA IS WEIRD. THIS GARFIELD IS LIKE A TOTAL STRANGER TO ME

I KNOW NOTHING ABOUT HIM

ASIDE FROM WHAT THE CREEP DID TO MY BODY
JIM DAVIS 2-9

THIS SHOULD JOG YOUR MEMORY, GARFIELD... LASAGNA!

NO THANK YOU. YOU WOULDN'T HAVE A PLUMP, JUICY MOUSE, WOULD YOU?

ARRRGH!
I'D NEVER GET THIS STUFF OUT OF MY WHISKERS
JIM DAVIS 2-10

Forget me not

YOU JUST **HAVE** TO RESTORE GARFIELD'S MEMORY, DOC

HE DOESN'T BEAT UP ON ODIE. HE DOESN'T CLAW THE FURNITURE. HE'S NOT LAZY AND OBNOXIOUS...
© 1987 United Feature Syndicate, Inc.
JIM DAVIS

ARE YOU SURE YOU WANT ME TO DO THIS?
COME TO THINK OF IT...
2-11

LET'S TEST HIS REFLEXES
DONK!
JIM DAVIS 2-12

© 1987 United Feature Syndicate, Inc.

NORMAL
FOR GARFIELD
DOING!

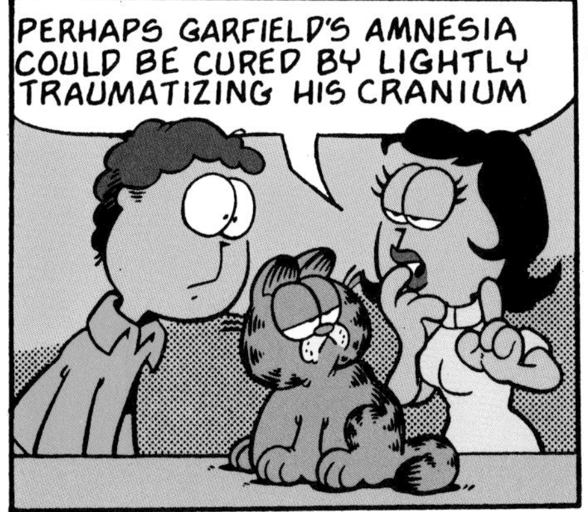
PERHAPS GARFIELD'S AMNESIA COULD BE CURED BY LIGHTLY TRAUMATIZING HIS CRANIUM

KNOCK MY CAT ON THE HEAD?! WHO WOULD EVER DO SUCH A THING?!!
© 1987 United Feature Syndicate, Inc.

MAY I BE OF ASSISTANCE?
YOU STAY OUT OF THIS
JIM DAVIS 2-13

GO AHEAD. A LITTLE TAP ON THE HEAD MAY BRING YOUR CAT'S MEMORY BACK
DONK!

GONK!
JIM DAVIS
© 1987 United Feature Syndicate, Inc.

HEY! I CAN REMEMBER! IT'S ME! GARFIELD THE CAT!
GARFIELD? WHO'S GARFIELD?
2-14

Happiness is a warm sunbeam

Draw it with Jon

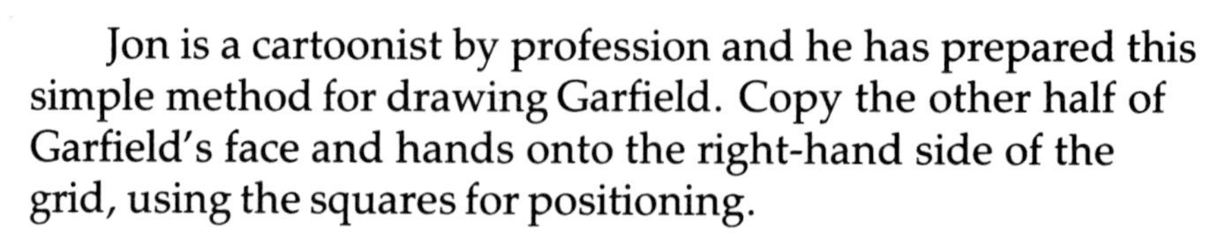

Jon is a cartoonist by profession and he has prepared this simple method for drawing Garfield. Copy the other half of Garfield's face and hands onto the right-hand side of the grid, using the squares for positioning.

When your picture is complete, it can be coloured.

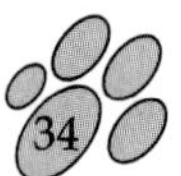

The GHOST of Christmas Presents

It was early Christmas Eve
In the house of Jon Arbuckle.
"Wonder where my prezzies are?"
Said Garfield with a chuckle.

Garfield wanted loads of stuff
Put under the Christmas Tree –
Toys, games, books; good things to eat,
"A mountain all for ME!"

So Garfield searched around the house,
The kitchen and the hall;
He even tried the garden shed:
No parcels there at all!

Cried Garfield: "I know where they are!
I bet they're in the attic!"
He climbed the stair and found them there.
Garfield was ecstatic!

Everything he'd asked for
Was there, wrapped beautifully.
"'Tis better to get than to receive!'"
He giggled, greedily.

Then all at once the door blew shut.
The light flicked on and off.
"What's happening here?"
poor Garfield cried.
"Cut out the spooky stuff!"

"Don't be scared," a strange voice said,
"I come to bring a warning.
Your selfish ways will bring no love
Or joy on Christmas morning!"

"W-W-Who are you?" gasped the trembling cat,
Against the door hard-pressing.
"I'm the ghost of Mr Scrooge.
I've already learned *my* lesson!"

"Your motto's wrong," the ghost went on,
"'Tis better to *give* than to get.
I've brought you here to tell you this –
Make sure you don't forget!"

Garfield looked at Mr Scrooge,
Then at his pile of stuff.
"Okay, okay! Please go away!
I've really heard enough!"

The attic door flew open
And Garfield rushed headlong.
"I must find gifts for Odie,
Pooky, Arlene and Jon."

Garfield rushed out to the shops.
He yelled: "This isn't funny!
The shops are just about to shut;
Whats more, I have no money!"

Garfield trudged back to the house,
His heart full of dismay.
"I've got no prezzies for my friends!
Wish I could end this day!"

On his doorstep Garfield found
A little Santa's hat.
He picked it up and put it on.
Then cried, "Hey! What is that?"

A pile of parcels had appeared
Beside his wooden bed.
'To Jon from Garfield' and so on –
That's what the labels said!

Garfield gave a whoop of joy!
"Old Scrooge has saved the day!
He's left a pile of Christmas gifts
For me to give away!"

Jon got socks and Odie a ball.
"They're not the least bit spooky,"
laughed Santa Garfield, giving out
A gift to his friend, Pooky.

So Garfield learned his lesson,
At Christmas, anyway.
"On New Year's Eve, I'll give some thought
To what my birthday list might say!"

Can you fill in the names of these 10 baby animals? If you complete the grid, your answers will spell something to do with Nermal.

Solution on page 56

1. A young horse
2. A baby lion or tiger
3. A young hare
4. A baby bird just learning to fly
5. A young duck
6. A young goose
7. A little swan
8. A little pig
9. A young eagle
10. A baby deer

GARFIELD®

RATS! THE WASHER'S BROKEN
FFT!
BANG!
UGH!

COME ON, GARFIELD, WE HAVE TO GO TO THE LAUNDROMAT

NO, JON! PLEASE ANYWHERE BUT THERE

YOU KNOW WHAT THAT PLACE IS LIKE! ESPECIALLY ON WEEKENDS
JIM DAVIS 3-8

I'LL GET HIM FOR THIS
Out of Ord

RIIINNNGG
Z
JIM DAVIS 2-16

SMASH!
© 1987 United Feature Syndicate, Inc.

I HATE ALARM CLOCKS

I HATE SPIDERS!
JIM DAVIS 2-17
© 1987 United Feature Syndicate, Inc.

STOMP!

I HATE HATING SPIDERS

JIM DAVIS 2-18

© 1987 United Feature Syndicate, Inc.

I HATE WAX DOUGHNUTS

JIM DAVIS 2-19

FWANG!
© 1987 United Feature Syndicate, Inc.

I HATE FOLDING CHAIRS

Bored on the fourth of July

© 1987 United Feature Syndicate, Inc.

© 1987 United Feature Syndicate, Inc.

© 1987 United Feature Syndicate, Inc.

ARRRGH!
JIM DAVIS

IT WAS ONLY A DREAM! IT WAS ONLY A DREAM! IT WAS ONLY A DREAM!
3-3

GARFIELD, I JUST DON'T KNOW WHAT I SEE IN YOU
IT IS A BIT OVERWHELMING, ISN'T IT?
3-4

YOU'RE RUDE, OBNOXIOUS, FAT, SELFISH, EGOTISTICAL, AND TOTALLY DEVOID OF ANY CHARM

I AM NOT EGOTISTICAL
JIM DAVIS

ARLENE, I THINK IT'S TIME WE GET SERIOUS
YOU DO?
JIM DAVIS

YES, SERIOUS ABOUT GETTING THAT GAP BETWEEN YOUR TEETH FIXED

THE TRUTH HURTS
3-5

I LOVE IT WHEN JON BAKES A CAKE
JIM DAVIS 3-7

'CAUSE I GET TO LICK THE ICING OUT OF THE BOWL

GARFIELD!!
OF COURSE, HE'D PREFER I WAIT TILL AFTER HE'S ICED THE CAKE

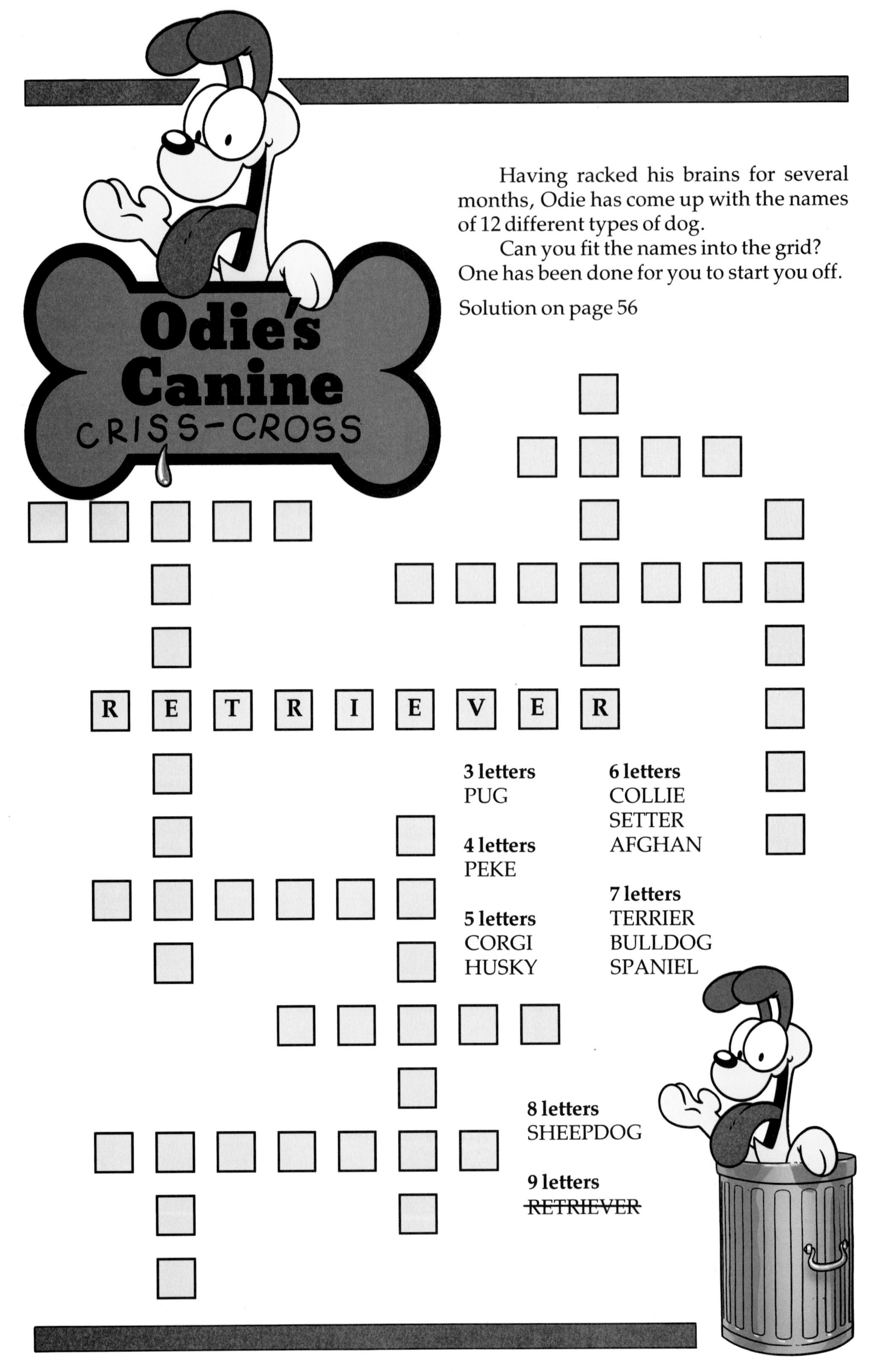

Having racked his brains for several months, Odie has come up with the names of 12 different types of dog.

Can you fit the names into the grid? One has been done for you to start you off.

Solution on page 56

3 letters
PUG

4 letters
PEKE

5 letters
CORGI
HUSKY

6 letters
COLLIE
SETTER
AFGHAN

7 letters
TERRIER
BULLDOG
SPANIEL

8 letters
SHEEPDOG

9 letters
~~RETRIEVER~~

Along with exercise, currants and Nermal, Garfield has a strong aversion to spiders. He usually gets the better of those he meets around the house, but he might not be so brave if he came upon certain other members of the species . . .

THE TARANTULA

Picturepoint – London

The tarantula is a huge, hairy spider found in southern Europe, the United States, Mexico and South America. Its body can grow up to 2 cm wide and its leg span is in the region of 12 cm. (That's about the size of a grown man's fist!) At one time tarantulas were thought to be poisonous, but this has now been shown not to be the case. They can be kept as pets, but need to be treated with caution, however, as they can inflict a very painful bite if annoyed. They also live for a very long time, some for about 30 years.

Tarantulas are unusual spiders in that they do not spin a web to catch their food. Instead, they pursue their prey along the ground. They feed mainly at night, eating insects, small frogs and toads, and mice.

THE BLACK WIDOW SPIDER

'Black widow' is the popular American name for a group of spiders also found in Africa, the Middle East, Australia and New Zealand. Unlike the tarantula, they are not very big, but they are greatly feared because of their poisonous bite. If you are unlucky enough to be attacked by a Black Widow, you will experience great pain, sickness and a difficulty in breathing. Fortunately, though, the bite is rarely fatal and most victims recover to tell the tale.

You seldom see a male Black Widow spider. The male is only a quarter the size of the female and is often killed and eaten by her after mating!

Picturepoint – London

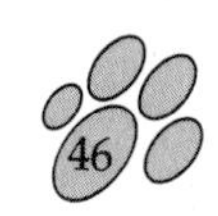

THE TRAP-DOOR SPIDER

© Oxford Scientific Films

This type of spider gets its name from its unique method of catching its food. Trap-door spiders dig a hole in the ground and then build a door at the top, hinged with silk. The spider hides inside the hole and, when it hears the vibrations of an approaching insect, it flips up the door, grabs its startled prey and drags it down into the hole.

These spiders, which are found in places as far apart as Japan and Africa, live deep down in their holes except when hunting food. Some holes have tunnels leading off the main tube and these may also have doors to the outside world.

THE BIRD-EATING SPIDER

Picturepoint – London

The Bird-Eating Spider is remarkable because of the size of the prey it is able to catch. As its name implies, this spider mainly eats small birds, but it has also been known to catch lizards, frogs and snakes. (To date there is no record of one catching a cat, so Garfield can relax in this case!) Bird-Eating Spiders have a pair of downward-pointing fangs which they sink into their victim and then inject with poison.

These tropical spiders also have an interesting form of defence. When attacked by a large bird or a hunting wasp, the Bird-Eating Spider kicks off the hairs from its back legs which irritate the eyes and nose of its enemy, making him retreat.

If you go down to the woods today...

Garfield SECRET STORY PUZZLE

These 6 words are all associated with Garfield:

CAT FUR TAIL SHEDDING FERN PASTA

They have been hidden in the following story. Can you find them?

The first one has been done for you.

Solution on page 56

"We're snowed in, Garfield!" cried Jon. "Oh, good," thought Garfield, "I can hibernate." "There's no food in the house," added Jon. "You ate it all." "Declare a state of emergency!" exclaimed Garfield. Just then, Odie bounded in, looking as happy as ever. "S**cat**, bonebreath!" yelled Garfield. "We've a problem here!"

Garfield set off round the house in search of things to eat. The fridge and the cupboards were bare. "I know how Old Mother Hubbard feels!" grumbled Garfield. Then he spied the cocktail cabinet. "Might be some packets of crisps in there!" he cried. But there was nothing but a half-empty bottle of flat lemonade. "This is past a joke!" exclaimed Garfield.

Meanwhile, in the sitting room, Jon had found a packet of biscuits that had rolled behind the sofa. Garfield crawled furtively along the ground, waiting to snatch them out of his master's hand. "Don't bother, Garfield," said Jon. "They're raisin cookies." "Yuck," said Garfield. He stomped over to the window and glared out at the blanket of gleaming white snow. "Infernal stuff!" he snapped.

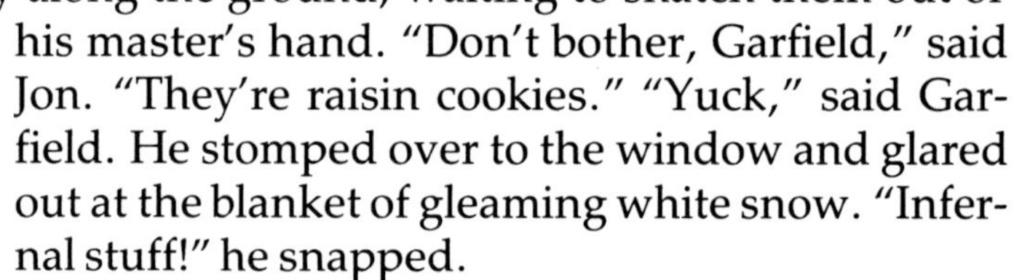

Moments later, Odie bounced in again. He had been looking for food in the garden shed. "Dingo brain!" yelled Garfield. "We can't eat a spade, a bag of sand and two tins of salt!"

"We can use them to escape!" cried Jon. "We can dig ourselves out with the spade; melt the snow with the salt, and sprinkle sand underfoot to walk on."

So Jon was able to get to the supermarket. "Odie, that was a surprisingly good idea," admitted Garfield. "But then, any time you get an idea, it's a surprise!"

GARFIELD®

KITTENS LOVE TO CHASE THINGS

THIS CAN BE A VERY SATISFYING FORM OF ENTERTAINMENT
CRASH!

KITTENS ALSO LOVE TO PLAY CATCH
BONK!
© 1987 United Feature Syndicate, Inc.

BUT, THE BEST WAY TO DRIVE THEM WILD IS TO HIDE OBJECTS FROM THEM
JIM DAVIS 1-18

ROWR!
CRUNCH!
HISS!

BUT, NOT FOR VERY LONG

GARFIELD, MEET THE NEWEST MEMBER OF OUR FAMILY, SWEETY BIRD
JIM DAVIS 3-30

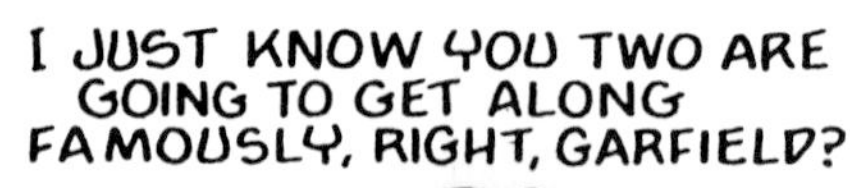
I JUST KNOW YOU TWO ARE GOING TO GET ALONG FAMOUSLY, RIGHT, GARFIELD?

RIGHT. SURE. UH, WOULD YOU HAPPEN TO HAVE A LIGHT FOR MY CUTTING TORCH?

HELLO. I'M SWEETY BIRD. I SING SWEET HAPPY SONGS TO BRIGHTEN YOUR MORNING

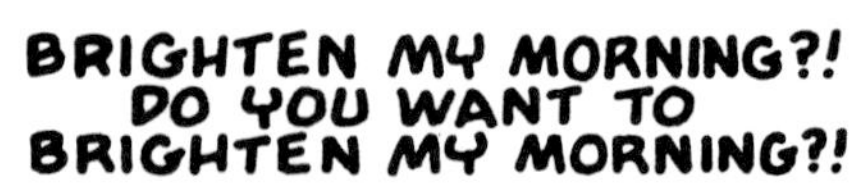
BRIGHTEN MY MORNING?! DO YOU WANT TO BRIGHTEN MY MORNING?!

JIM DAVIS 3-31

THEN YOU CAN MARCH OUT OF THAT CAGE AND CRAWL BETWEEN TWO SLICES OF BREAD
JON!

GARFIELD, DO YOU LIKE SWEETY BIRD?
HE'S RIGHT UP THERE WITH DOGS AND MONDAYS

YOU WOULDN'T INTEND HIM ANY HARM, WOULD YOU?
I DON'T KNOW WHAT YOU'RE TALKING ABOUT

THEN WHY IS HE COVERED WITH CLAM SAUCE?
AN OLD FAMILY RECIPE
JIM DAVIS 4-1

SQUAWK!
JIM DAVIS 4-2

HONK!

DID WE REMEMBER HOW TO OPEN THE BIRD CAGE?
NOT ONLY THAT, WE FORGOT BIRDS COULD FLY

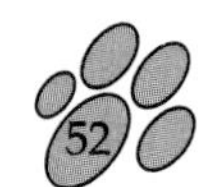

HEY, BIRD! YOU THINK YOU'RE SAFE OUT THERE, HUH?

WELL, I HAVE A LITTLE TREAT FOR YOU!
© 1987 United Feature Syndicate, Inc.
JIM DAVIS 4-3

HAVE YOU, PERCHANCE, EVER HEARD A CAT SCREAM?

HEY, GARFIELD! WHAT ARE YOU DOING OUT THERE?

AND LOOK! SWEETY BIRD'S ON YOUR HEAD!
JIM DAVIS 4-4

WHERE'S MY CAMERA?!
I LOATHE LIFE
© 1987 United Feature Syndicate, Inc.

GC Gluttons Club Card
GARFIELD
Credit me with some intelligence!

HURRY, GARFIELD, THE TV WORKOUT SHOW IS ABOUT TO START!

YOU PROMISED YOU'D TRY IT, SO LET'S GO
OKAY, BUT FIRST ANSWER ME THIS...
© 1987 United Feature Syndicate, Inc.

JUST HOW THE HECK AM I SUPPOSED TO MOVE?
JIM DAVIS 4-6

GARFIELD!

YOU SHREDDED MY RUNNING SHOES!
SOMEDAY YOU'LL THANK ME FOR THAT, JON
© 1987 United Feature Syndicate, Inc.

JOGGING'S THE DISEASE. I'M THE CURE
JIM DAVIS 4-7

OKAY, STAND UP STRAIGHT AND PUT YOUR HANDS ON YOUR HIPS

THOSE OF YOU TOO FAT TO FIND YOUR HIPS JUST GIVE IT YOUR BEST GUESS

I HATE SARCASTIC FITNESS INSTRUCTORS
© 1987 United Feature Syndicate, Inc.
JIM DAVIS 4-8

NOW FOR JUMPING JACKS ON THE TWO COUNT
JIM DAVIS 4-9

ONE!
CRASH!
© 1987 United Feature Syndicate, Inc.

OH, BY THE WAY, BEFORE WE GET TO TWO, DON'T TRY THIS EXERCISE ON A RECENTLY POLISHED FLOOR
NOW HE TELLS ME

THAT'S GOOD, EVERYBODY. PUSH UP!

...AND DOWN!
© 1987 United Feature Syndicate, Inc.

...AND UP!...
I WAS BUILT FOR PUSH-UPS
JIM DAVIS 4-10

NO, SERIOUSLY, LINDA, I'M A FUN GUY. I DO GREAT IMPRESSIONS!

YOU DO IMPRESSIONS TOO? LET'S HEAR ONE

LISTEN TO THIS, GARFIELD. SHE SOUNDS JUST LIKE A DIAL TONE!
THIS MAN HAS NO BRAIN
JIM DAVIS 4-11

YOU'RE A SLOB, GARFIELD. WHY CAN'T YOU STAY AS CLEAN AS OTHER CATS?
GARFIELD

YOU'RE SUPPOSED TO WASH YOURSELF LIKE THIS
OH, VERY WELL
GARFIELD

START WITH THIS ARM AND MAKE IT SNAPPY. YOU HAVE A LOT OF TERRITORY TO COVER
GARFIELD
JIM DAVIS 4-13

DO YOU KNOW WHAT I HATE MOST ABOUT THIS BED?

UNNNGH!

TRYING TO SLEEP ON MY BACK
JIM DAVIS 4-15

IT'S TIME TO GET UP
JIM DAVIS 4-16

CREAK!
CRACK!

IT'S ALSO TIME TO GO ON A DIET

Garfield's Cat Conundrum
(page 18)
1. CATERPILLAR
2. CATASTROPHE
3. CATTLE
4. CATALOGUE
5. CAT'S CRADLE
6. CATCHPHRASE
7. CATHEDRAL
8. CATAPULT
9. CATAMARAN
10. CATKIN
11. CATACOMB
12. CATHERINE WHEEL
13. CATERING
14. CATCALL
15. CATARRH
16. CATEGORY
17. CATCH
18. CATS' EYES
19. CATARACT
20. CATERWAUL

Garfield's Fast Food Quiz
(pages 22 and 23)
1. (b) Italy
2. (c) Hot
3. (b) Chili pepper
4. (a) True
5. (a) Beansprouts
6. (a) Frankfurter
7. (c) Wimpy
8. Fish and chips
9. Kebab
10. True
11. (b) Coca-Cola
12. He would be pleased. It's a large ice-cream sundae!

Arlene's Beauty Wordsearch
(page 26) Missing item: SHOES

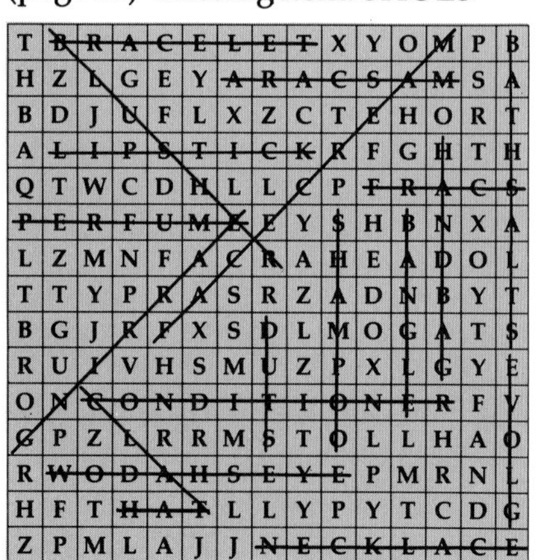

Nermal's Young Animal Puzzle
(page 38)
Words connected with Nermal: CUTE KITTEN

COLT
CUB
LEVERET
FLEDGELING
DUCKLING
GOSLING
CYGNET
PIGLET
EAGLET
FAWN

Odie's Canine Criss-Cross
(page 44)

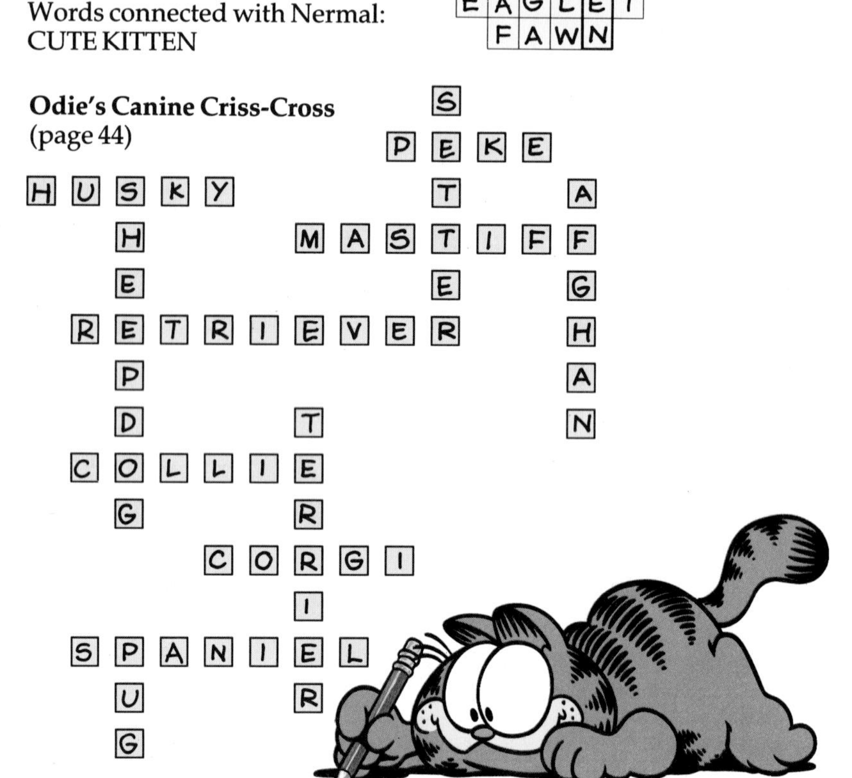

Garfield's Secret Story Puzzle
(page 50)

"We're snowed in, Garfield!" cried Jon. "Oh, good," thought Garfield, "I can hibernate." "There's no food in the house," added Jon, "you ate it all." "Declare a state of emergency!" exclaimed Garfield. Just then, Odie bounded in, looking as happy as ever. "S**cat**, bone-breath!" yelled Garfield. "We've a problem here!"

Garfield set off round the house in search of things to eat. The fridge and the cupboards were bare. "I know how Old Mother Hubbard feels!" grumbled Garfield. Then he spied the cock**tail** cabinet. "Might be some packets of crisps in there!" he cried. But there was nothing but a half-empty bottle of flat lemonade. "This is **past a** joke!" exclaimed Garfield.

Meanwhile, in the sitting room, Jon had found a packet of biscuits that had rolled behind the sofa. Garfield crawled **fur**tively along the ground, waiting to snatch them out of his master's hand. "Don't bother, Garfield," said Jon. "They're raisin cookies." "Yuck," said Garfield. He stomped over to the window and glared out at the blanket of gleaming white snow. "In**fern**al stuff!" he snapped.

Moments later, Odie bounced in again. He had been looking for food in the garden **shed**. "**Ding**o brain!" yelled Garfield. "We can't eat a spade, a bag of sand and two tins of salt!"

"We can use them to escape!" cried Jon. "We can dig ourselves out with the spade; melt the snow with the salt, and sprinkle sand underfoot to walk on."

So Jon was able to get to the supermarket. "Odie, that was a surprisingly good idea," admitted Garfield. "But then, any time you get an idea, it's a surprise!"

A MIDSUMMER NIGHT'S SCREAM

"Hey, Garfield!" called Jon. "Do you know what day it is today?"
"Christmas?" cried Garfield, hopefully.
"It's Midsummer's Day," said Jon.
"Close!" said Garfield.
"Tonight," whispered Jon, excitedly, "the forests are full of magic . . ."
"I only believe in fairy **cakes,"** put in Garfield.
". . . and things are said to come alive!"
"Like Odie's brain?" queried Garfield.

Jon and Garfield were sitting in the garden, finishing lunch. (100 hot dogs – 99 for Garfield and 1 for Jon. Garfield believes in sharing).

"Oh, Garfield," sighed Jon, stretching his arms, "don't these long, hot summer days make you want to go somewhere?"

"Yes," said Garfield. "They make me want to go to sleep."

"Let's go somewhere this afternoon," suggested Jon. "There's a new Amusement Park on the other side of town. Why don't we give it a whirl?"

"I can hardly contain my indifference," yawned Garfield.

"We could take a picnic tea," added Jon.

"Suppose I could be persuaded," said Garfield.

Jon bundled Garfield and Odie into the car and set off for the Amusement Park. On the way, Garfield pretended to be a basking shark.

"Might be able to filter a few birds as we go along," he murmured.

"We're nearly there now, boys!" exclaimed Jon. "I can see the flags fluttering out of the corner of my eye."

"That's Odie's tongue, you bird-brain!" groaned Garfield.

Jon parked the car, paid the entrance fee and went into the park with his pets. "There's so much here!" he cried. "What would you like to do first?"

"Let's eat!" suggested Garfield.

Jon took Garfield and Odie on all the rides. They went on the Water Splash, the Wall of Death and the Giant Slide. Then they went on the Foaming River, the Go-Karts, the Helter-skelter and the Bumper Boats.

"Isn't this fun?" whooped Jon.

"Mind-blowing," grumbled Garfield.

"What next?" cried Jon. "How about a visit to The Valley of the Dinosaurs?"

"Noooo, thanks," gulped Garfield, shaking his head. 'Those big, plastic dinosaurs are far too realistic."

"Got it!" exclaimed Jon. "Let's go on the Big Dipper. It's the biggest ride of all."

Immediately, Garfield clutched his stomach.

"Feel queasy, eh Garfield?" said Jon. "Okay, then. You sit this one out. I'll go on with Odie."

Jon left Garfield guarding the picnic basket while he and Odie joined the queue for the Big Dipper. "So long, Jon." said Garfield. He eyed the picnic basket. "Like they always say, 'A fool and his lunch are soon parted!'"

Waiting until his friends were out of sight, Garfield whipped the cover off the picnic basket. "Only good thing about fresh air," he murmured, "it fine-tunes the appetite to the point of perfection." Garfield got into the picnic basket before starting to eat. "I like to be amongst friends," he said. Garfield set about his task with a vengence, scoffing the entire picnic in the time it took Jon and Odie to move up one place in the queue.

"Now for a nap," yawned Garfield.

Garfield drifted off to sleep. The next thing he knew was a finger prodding him in the stomach and a voice bellowing, "You greedy cat!" in his ear.

"Jon appears to be back," gasped Garfield.

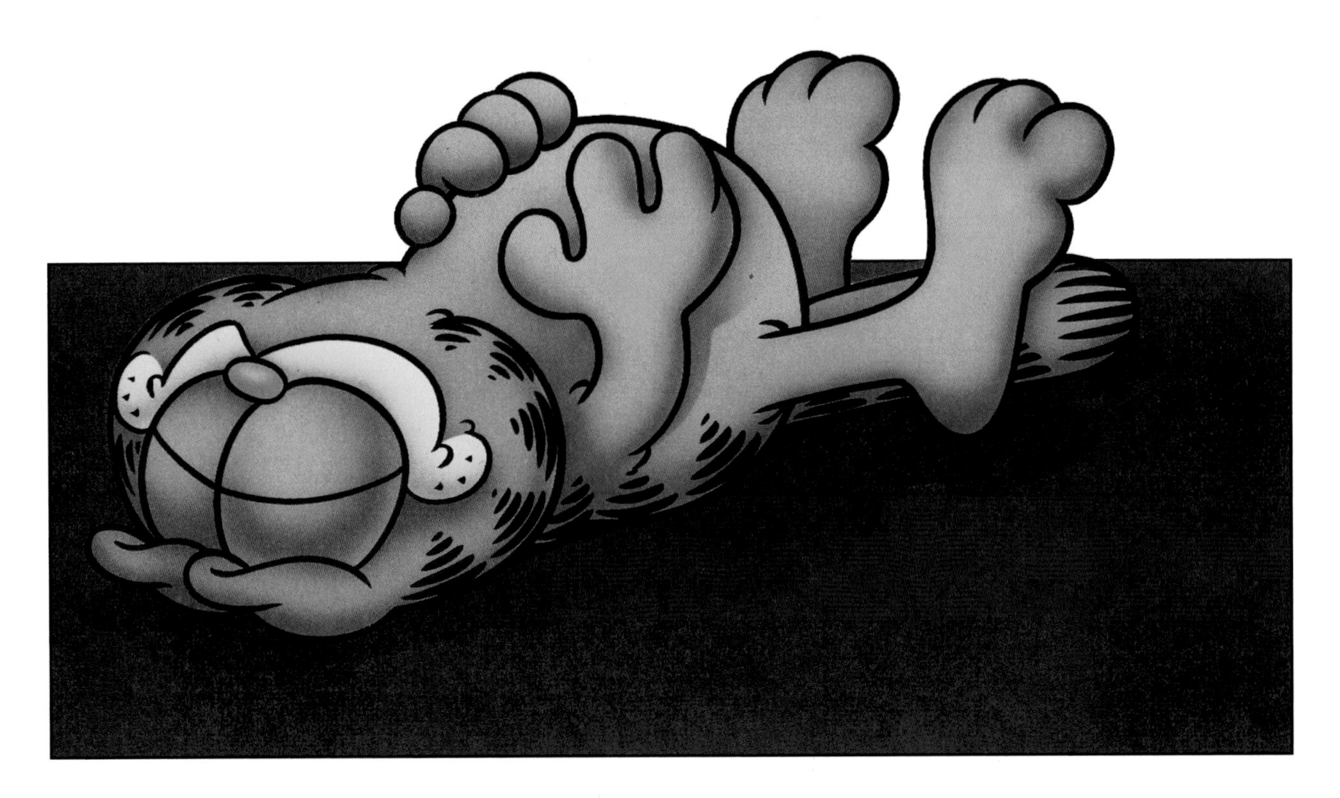

Garfield shot out of the picnic basket like a scalded rabbit and charged off round the Amusement Park with Jon in hot pursuit. For the next hour, they played cat-and-mouse amongst the stalls and sideshows. "And I'm not the cat!" puffed Garfield. Eventually, Garfield dived into a small, leafy valley that offered lots of hiding-places.

"Safe at last!" he sighed.

Garfield felt even more tired than before after all the chasing about, so he found himself a cosy spot in a clearing, folded his paws over his very full stomach and went into a deep sleep. Above him, the sky slowly changed from blue to orange as the sun set. Then it began to get dark.

Meanwhile, Jon was frantically looking for his missing pet. "You go that way, Odie," said Jon. "I'll go this. We'll search the place one last time."

Still there was no sign of Garfield. "We'll have to give up," sighed Jon. "The park closes in five minutes. Maybe Garfield will find his own way home."

Whimpering anxiously, Odie got into the car. But, as Jon started the engine, Odie wound down the window and jumped out. He raced back to the park and squeezed through the gates just before they clanged shut. Jon followed him.

"I'm sorry, sir," said the attendant. "The park is now closed."

"But my pets are inside!" protested Jon.

"Come back for them in the morning," suggested the attendant. "They'll come to no harm tonight."

After a lot of sniffing around, Odie picked up Garfield's scent-trail. (Eau-de-lasagne is quite unmistakable!) He tracked his friend to the woods and woke him up by licking his face. "Ugh! It's raining!" spluttered Garfield. Then he spotted Odie beside him, wagging his tail like a windscreen wiper. "What are you looking so happy about?" muttered Garfield. "It's the middle of the night and we're lost."

Garfield stumbled around through the undergrowth, trying to find out where they were. Suddenly, the moon came out from behind a cloud, illuminating a sign in the distance. It said: VALLEY OF THE DINOSAURS.

"It's okay, Odie," called Garfield. "We're in that dinosaur place."

Then Garfield stopped and his eyes grew wide with fear. "D-D-Dinosaur place," he gulped.

Garfield raced back to Odie who had already started to whimper. He pointed his paw at the nearest model dinosaur that towered above their heads.

"Don't be silly," scoffed Garfield. "'Course it's not moving!" Next moment, the monster turned its head and looked down at the tiny, trembling pair with one yellow eye. "Don't worry," yelled Garfield. "It's only a Diplodocus. They just eat leaves!"

Garfield and Odie fled through the woods as all the dinosaurs started to move. "It's that Midsummer's Night business," cried Garfield. "It's brought these prehistoric lardballs to life!" Garfield and Odie avoided the huge, crashing feet and sharp, gnashing teeth for a while, then a giant scaley claw lifted Odie fifty feet into the air. Looking up, Garfield found himself staring at the fierce face of a Tyrannosaurus Rex, the most fearsome dinosaur the world has ever known.

"Leave him alone, fossil-features!" shouted Garfield.

The dinosaur took no notice of Garfield's futile threats. Instead, he held Odie in one gigantic hand, relishing the tasty morsel he was about to swallow. Garfield felt himself getting more and more angry. "Put him down, you big bully!" he yelled. "He's not very bright, but he's my friend. And you won't like him – he's all slobbery!"

As Garfield watched the Tyrannosaurus opening his jaws to swallow Odie, something strange happened. Garfield began to change shape! "My head's getting bigger," he gasped, "and my stomach's enormous! I haven't eaten anything for hours (and don't I know it!) W-W-What's going on?"

The Midsummer magic was working on Garfield, too. He had turned into a GARFIELDOSAURUS! Fangs gleaming and claws slashing, he gave battle to the Tyrannosaurus who turned and fled in terror. Odie was saved!

As dawn broke, the dinosaurs lumbered back to their places and froze into their usual poses. Garfield also returned to normal. "Pity, really," he murmured. "Think of the power-eating I could have done."

Jon was waiting outside the gates as the Amusement Park opened for another day. "Ah, there you are!" he cried, as Garfield and Odie scampered out to meet him. Jon opened the car door for his pets. "I'll take you home for a monster breakfast," he beamed. "Could you phrase that differently?" mumbled Garfield.

After breakfast, Odie kept licking Garfield's face. "Odie's thanking you for something, Garfield," said Jon. "What exactly happened last night?"

"I don't remember, "murmured Garfield, sleepily. "It's ancient history now!"

GARFIELD